The Joy of
Organ Classics

Edited by Stephen Duro.

Yorktown Music Press / Music Sales Limited
London / New York / Paris / Sydney / Copenhagen / Madrid

Exclusive Distributors:
Music Sales Limited
8/9 Frith Street, London W1V 5TZ, England.
Music Sales Pty Limited
120 Rothschild Avenue, Rosebery, NSW 2018, Australia.
Music Sales Corporation
257 Park Avenue South, New York, NY10010, United States of America.

This book © Copyright 1994 by Yorktown Music Press / Music Sales Limited
Order No. AM91842
ISBN 0-7119-3954-3

Cover art direction by Michael Bell Design.
Cover illustration by Vikki Liogier.
Music edited by Stephen Duro.
Music processed by Allegro Reproductions.

Music Sales' complete catalogue describes thousands of titles and is available in
full colour sections by subject, direct from Music Sales Limited.
Please state your areas of interest and send a cheque / postal order for £1.50 for postage to:
Music Sales Limited, Newmarket Road, Bury St. Edmunds, Suffolk IP33 3YB.

Printed in the United Kingdom by
J.B. Offset Printers (Marks Tey) Limited, Marks Tey, Essex.

Adagio

Composed by Franz Liszt

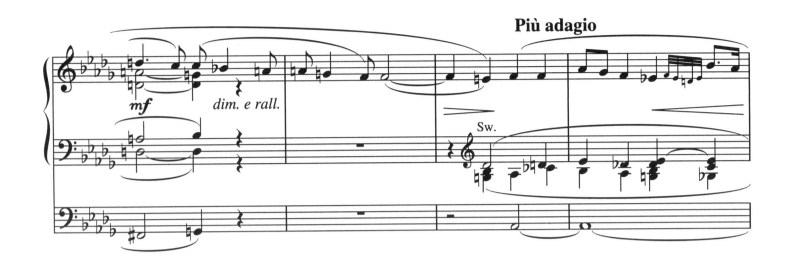

Più adagio

Adagio molto

6

Air

Composed by Samuel Wesley

Allegro Maestoso e Vivace
from Sonata No.3

Composed by Felix Mendelssohn-Bartholdy

Contrapunctus No.1
from The Art Of Fugue

Composed by Johann Sebastian Bach

Andante Tranquillo
from Sonata No.3

Composed by Felix Mendelssohn-Bartholdy

19

Behold, A Rose Is Blooming

Composed by Johannes Brahms

21

Come, Saviour Of The Gentiles

Composed by Johann Sebastian Bach

Canonic Study in B Major Op.56

Composed by Robert Schumann

28

29

Gavotte

Composed by Samuel Wesley

31

Fantasia in C Minor

Composed by Johann Sebastian Bach

33

Hornpipe from Water Music

Composed by Georg Frideric Handel

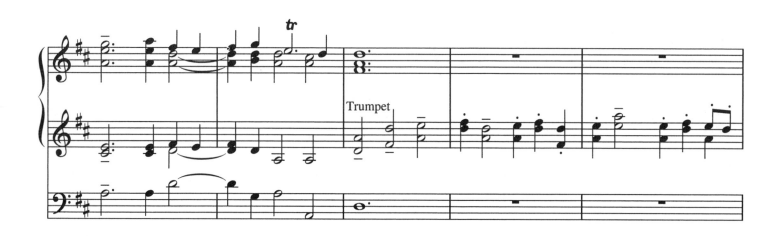

Jesu Joy Of Man's Desiring

Composed by Johann Sebastian Bach

Andante grazioso

43

45

Larghetto from
Concerto Grosso No.12

Composed by Georg Frideric Handel

47

March from Scipio

Composed by Georg Frideric Handel

49

Nimrod from Enigma Variations

Composed by Edward Elgar

Prelude & Fugue in F

Composed by Dietrich Buxtehude

L'istesso tempo

Prelude in F

Composed by Charles Villiers Stanford

Allegretto

Trumpet Tune And Air

Composed by Henry Purcell